My First Reader Series — Book Three

Alvin and Amelia's

Busy Summer

Katie Weber

My First Reader Series — Book Three

Alvin and Amelia's

Busy Summer

Katie Weber

Ridgeway Publishing
Medina, New York

ALVIN AND AMELIA'S BUSY SUMMER

My First Reader Series — Book Three

Copyright © 2015 Ridgeway Publishing

First Printing 2015

*To order additional
copies, please visit
your local bookstore
or contact:*

**Ridgeway Publishing
3161 Fruit Ave.
Medina NY 14103
ph: (888) 822-7894
fax: (585) 798-9016**

ISBN# 978-0-9906655-8-8

Printed in the United States of America

Table of Contents

My New Words

robin

window

windowsill

bowl

cherries

hatch

upstairs

The Robin

"See that Robin," said Alvin. "Did you see what that robin had in its beak?"

"No," said Amelia.

"It had grass in its beak," said Alvin.

"That means the robin is building a nest."

"Look!" said Amelia. "There it goes again! Look Alvin, the robin flew up to the window."

The children watched the robin. The robin flew down to the ground. It took some dead grass in its beak. Then if flew up to the window. It used the grass to build a nest on the windowsill.

"Let's go to the house," said Alvin. "We will go upstairs. We will go to the window. We can see the robin building the nest."

The children ran to the house. They ran up the stairs.

"Oh, look!" said Amelia. "The nest looks like a little bowl."

The children watched the robin fly away to get more grass. Back and forth, back and forth flew the robin.

"I like robins," said Amelia. "Robins are pretty."

"Robins are pretty," said Alvin. "They look pretty but they eat cherries. Maybe Mother and Father will not want the robin to live here."

Amelia got a very sad look on her face. "I

hope Mother and Father will let the robin stay here. I want the robin to live here. I will ask Mother if the robin may live here."

Amelia ran to find Mother. "Mother! Mother! May the robin stay here? May the robin build a nest on the windowsill?"

"Yes, the robin may stay," said Mother. "You will have fun to watch the robin. The robin will lay eggs in the nest. Baby robins will hatch from the eggs. You will have fun to watch."

"Oh, good!" said Amelia. "I am so happy. I am so happy that the robin may stay."

My New Words

string

straight

radishes

carrots

peas

sprout

Planting

Mother was putting things into a basket.

"What is that?" asked Amelia.

"Seeds," said Mother. "I want to plant some seeds."

"May I help?" asked Amelia. "Mother may I help to plant the seeds?"

"Yes, you may help," said Mother. "We will go to the garden. We will plant the seeds in the garden."

"Do I need my coat?" asked Amelia.

"No," said Mother. "It is warm today. You do not need your coat."

Mother and Amelia walked to the garden. Rover came too.

"Go away!" said Amelia. "Go away! Rover you cannot help to plant seeds."

"Rover may come too," said Mother. "He cannot help to plant the seeds but he can watch when we plant them."

Mother got a hoe. She got a string. The string helped her to make a straight row.

"Now you may plant some peas," said Mother. "Put the seeds in like this." Mother showed Amelia how to plant the peas.

Amelia

was happy. She was happy to plant the seeds. She dropped the little pink seeds into the row.

Mother took the hoe. She made some more rows then she helped Amelia to plant peas.

When they were finished with the peas, they planted carrots and radishes. Mother put the hoe and string away. "We are finished for today," she said. "We will stop now. Come Amelia, it is time to go to the house now."

"I want to watch the garden grow," said Amelia. "I want to stay here and watch the peas grow."

"The peas will not grow now," said Mother. "It will take some time for the peas to grow. First they must sprout, then they will grow. We must wait at least a week before we will see plants growing."

"I do not want to stay that long," said Amelia. "I will come to the house with you now."

My New Words

scared

thunder

lightning

weather

flashed

splashed

rainbow

promised

remember

Colors in the Sky

Amelia was afraid. Alvin was afraid too.

"You do not have to be scared," said Mother. "God will take care of us."

"I don't like the thunder," said Alvin. "It is so loud."

"I don't like the lightning," said Amelia.

"Who makes the thunder and lightning?" asked Mother.

"I don't know," said Amelia.

"I think God does," said Alvin. "God makes the weather, so He makes the thunder and lightning too."

"It is dark," said Amelia. "Does God make it dark?"

"Yes," said Alvin. "It is dark because it is going to rain soon."

Just then the rain started. It rained fast. The lightning flashed and the thunder crashed. Alvin and Amelia stood beside Mother. The rain splashed and splashed.

Then the lightning stopped. The thunder stopped. The rain slowed down. The sky was not as dark anymore.

"I will go and play now," said Alvin. "I am not afraid now."

Amelia stayed with Mother. She watched the rain falling slowly. Then the sun started shining. It shone down on the wet earth. It shone on the falling rain.

"Look! A rainbow!" said Mother.

"Oh it is pretty!" said Amelia. "Come

Alvin!"

She pointed to the colorful rainbow in the sky. "Did God make the rainbow?" she asked.

"Yes," said Mother. "There is a story in the Bible about the rainbow."

"I know that story," said Alvin. "When Noah came out of the ark, God put a rainbow in the sky."

"Why did He?" asked Amelia.

"It was to tell Noah something," said Alvin. "It was to tell him that God would never again send a flood to cover all the earth."

"That happened a long, long time ago," said Mother, "but God has not forgotten the people on the earth. He promised that He will always take care of us."

"You said that He takes care of us when it thunders," said Amelia. "The next time that it thunders I will try to remember God's promise."

Rhyme Time

Noah's family
Was safe in the ark,
The rain fell down
And the sky was dark.

The rain was over
And the green grass grew,
Out came Noah-
The animals too.

God set in the sky
The colorful bow,
God's promise for
Noah, down below.

Tis a promise still
For each one today,
God cares for us
In every way.

My New Words

shout

surprise

dress

another

A Blue Surprise

"Come Amelia. Come Alvin!" said
Mother. "I want you to go find a surprise."

"Surprise! Surprise!" said Amelia. "I like
a surprise!"

"What is it?" asked Alvin. "What is it and
where is it?"

Mother laughed. "I will let you try to find
it. The surprise is blue. It is little."

"Blue and little," said Alvin.

"Blue and little," said Amelia. "Is it a new dress? Did you make a new dress for me?"

"No," said Mother. "It is not a dress."

"Is it something to eat?" asked Alvin.

"No," said Mother.

"Is it something to play with?" asked Amelia.

"No," said Mother.

"Is it in here?" asked Alvin.

"No," said Mother. "You must look outside."

The children looked outside. They looked and looked but they could not find a little blue surprise.

"It is in something," said Mother. "It is in something brown."

"I know!" said Amelia. "You said the surprise is blue. The sky is blue. Is that the surprise, Mother? Is the sky the surprise?"

"No," said Mother.

"The sky is not little," said Alvin. "The

sky is not a surprise. We see the sky every day."

"You cannot see the surprise here," said Mother. "Go to another window. Find the blue surprise."

The children ran to this window. They ran to that window. They ran here and they ran there, but they could not find the surprise.

"You did not try all the windows," said Mother.

The children went upstairs. They ran to this window and they ran to that window.

"Oh! I see it!" shouted Alvin. "Look! Look!"

Amelia ran to Alvin. She saw what Alvin saw. "Eggs!" she shouted. "One, two, three, little, blue eggs! What a nice surprise."

Rhyme Time

The robin built a wee brown nest,
And laid some little blue thing in it,
I'm glad my house is not so wee,
Or I'd fall out any minute!

— My New Words —

picture

kite

guess

field

carried

wound

unwound

string

windy

handle

The Surprise in the Box

Father came home from town. He had a big box.

"What is it? What is it?" asked Alvin.

"I see something," said Amelia. "I see a picture on the box."

"Oh!" said Alvin. "Oh Father, is the thing in the box like the picture on the outside of the box? Is a kite in the box?"

Father laughed at Alvin and Amelia.

"There is a kite in the box," he said. "You guessed what is in the box."

"When can we fly it?" asked Alvin.

"We must wait for a windy day," said Father. "When it has more wind I will help you."

It was not windy the next day. The children waited. It was not windy the next day.

"I wish it would get windy," said Alvin.

That night it rained. It rained and rained. The trees blew in the wind. The rain came down fast.

It was windy in the morning. It was not raining fast, but it was still raining.

"It is windy!" said Alvin. "Now we can fly our kite."

"We must wait for the rain to stop," said Mother. "We will not fly the kite in the rain."

The rain kept on all morning. At noon it stopped and the sun came out. It was still windy.

After dinner the family went outside. They walked back to the field. Father carried the kite.

"Why do we go back here?" asked Amelia. "Why can we not fly our kite by the house and barn?"

"We must go away from the trees," said Father. "We do not want the kite to bump against something. It might break the kite if that happens."

When they got to the field they stopped. Father unwound some of the string. He threw the kite up into the air. He unwound some more string.

"Oh! Oh!" said Alvin.

"Oh! Oh!" said Amelia.

The kite went up in the sky. It went up and up. Alvin had a turn holding the string. He could feel the kite pulling on the string.

He let Amelia have a turn to hold the string. The kite looked like a small kite. It

did not look like a big kite now.

Father took the string. He wound the string onto the handle. The kite got bigger. Then he unwound the string and the kite got smaller. Again and again Father did this.

The children could have watched for a long time, but Father said he must get back to work. He wound and wound the string and the kite came down.

"What fun we had!" said Alvin.

"Yes," said Amelia. "flying a kite is fun!"

My New Words

daffodils

spring

springtime

tomorrow

basket

flowers

jar

creek

dandelions

weeds

hundreds

Picking Flowers

Father came into the house. He had some yellow flowers in his hand.

"I picked some daffodils for you," he said to Mother. "The daffodils down by the creek are blooming nicely."

"Spring is here," said Mother. "The daffodils are blooming and the robin has made a nest. I like springtime. I think I will plant some more tomorrow."

The next day Mother got her basket of seeds.

"May I help?" asked Amelia. "May I help to plant the garden?"

"You helped to plant the peas," said Mother. "You were a good help, but today I want to plant things that you cannot plant. You may come out and watch."

Amelia went to the garden with Mother. She watched Mother plant some seeds then she looked around. She saw very many flowers in the field. "Oh they are pretty!" she said to herself. She walked to the field. The flowers were yellow. There were hundreds and hundreds of flowers.

Amelia picked some flowers then she walked to the house. She got a jar then she put the yellow flowers into the jar. She set the jar in the middle of the table.

"This will be a nice surprise for Mother," she thought.

Mother came in. She saw the flowers. She

smiled at Amelia.

"Thank-you, Amelia," she said.

"There were very many flowers," said Amelia.

"Why did Father not pick those? Why did he go to the creek?"

Mother looked at Amelia. She saw Amelia's happy face. She did not want Amelia to feel unhappy.

"The flowers you picked are dandelions," she said. "Dandelions are weeds."

Amelia's smile turned upside down. She was not happy that she had picked weeds for Mother.

"I am happy with the dandelions. I know
that you picked them because you love me.
That jar of dandelions looks pretty. Thank-

you for picking them, Amelia."

Amelia's smile came back. Mother liked her flowers even if they were weeds. If Mother liked them then Amelia was happy. Amelia liked doing things for Mother.

My New Words

hatched

worm

waited

pink

mouth

cute

feathers

Baby Robins

"The eggs have hatched," said Alvin. "The robin's eggs have hatched."

"Did you see the little birds?" asked Amelia. "Alvin, did you see the little robins?"

"Yes," said Alvin. "When the robin flew away, I saw three little birds."

Amelia ran up the stairs. The mother bird was sitting on the nest. Amelia could not see the little birds.

"Wait!" said Alvin. "Just wait and you will see the baby birds. The mother robin will fly away. It will fly away to get a worm."

Amelia waited. She waited and waited. Then the robin flew away.

Amelia saw something in the nest. It was brown and pink, but it did not look like a robin.

Mother robin came back. She had a worm. The things in the nest moved. Something opened wide.

"Oh! Oh!" said Amelia. "The baby birds do not look like robins. They do not look nice. Look Alvin, they open their mouth. They open it far. The bird's mouth is as big as the bird!"

"They will grow," said Alvin. "The birds will grow bigger. They will grow feathers like mother robin. When they grow feathers they will look cute."

"I want them to grow," said Amelia. "I

want them to look cute."

The children looked at the robins every day. The baby robins grew. They got feathers. Soon the baby robins would fly away.

"The robins are cute now," said Amelia. "I wish they would stay here. I do not want them to fly away."

"A bird must fly," said Father. "When Emma was a baby she could not walk. When she grew bigger she learned to walk. A baby bird will learn to fly. When it can fly, it can get worms to eat. It does not want to stay in the nest all the time."

"I want to watch them fly," said Amelia. "I think they will be happy to fly away and find some worms."

My New Words

afternoon   drown

fence   careful

finished   hurried

colorful   count

chase   enough

pond   quacked

noisy

White Friends

"It is all ready," said Father. "The ducks will come this afternoon. The fence is finished and the pond is ready."

"What color are the ducks?" asked Amelia.

"They are white," said Father.

"I wish we'd get colorful ducks," said Alvin. "Colorful ducks would look so pretty on our pond."

"White ducks will look pretty too," said Father.

"Do you think Rover will chase the ducks?" asked Mother.

"I'm hoping he won't," said Father. "The gate must always be closed. Rover may never go to the pond."

"May we go to the pond?" asked Amelia.

"No," said Father. "You can look at the ducks from the fence. A pond is not a place for children to play. We want you to stay away from it."

"You would drown if you would fall into it." said Alvin.

"I would be careful," said Amelia. "I would not fall into it, but maybe Emma would."

"Even if we are careful we can slip and fall," said Mother. "You must all stay away from the pond."

That afternoon the ducks came. Everyone hurried outside. Father and

Mother helped to get the ducks from the truck.

Amelia tried to count the ducks, but she could not count fast enough.

Just then Rover came running. He barked and barked. He ran at the ducks. The ducks quacked. It was noisy. Rover barked. The ducks quacked. Emma cried.

Alvin ran to Rover. He patted Rover's neck. "Be a good dog," he said. "You must not bark at the ducks."

Father closed the gate. The ducks were safe, but Rover did not stop barking.

"He will get used to them," said Father. "Play with him and he will stop barking."

Alvin took Rover to the yard and played with him. Amelia and Emma looked through the fence. They watched the ducks go down to the pond.

Splash! The ducks splashed the water with their wings. Emma laughed. She liked to watch the ducks splash the water with their wings.

My New Words

drowning

catching

normal

matter

quietly

Amelia's Scare

Amelia ran to the house. She had been outside playing with Emma, but now she ran to the house. She must find Mother. She must tell Mother that something was the matter.

The door banged as Amelia pushed it close behind her.

"Not so noisy," said Mother. "Amelia I want you to close the door quietly when you come in."

"Oh Mother!" said Amelia. "You must come. You must come to the pond. Something is the matter. Something bad happened."

"Oh! Oh!" said Mother. "Is it Emma? Did Emma fall into the pond?"

"No! No!" said Amelia. "It is not Emma. It is the ducks! They... they... oh Mother, I don't know what is the matter!"

"Did Rover get the ducks? Did Rover chase the ducks?"

"No, it is not Rover. Rover is in the barn with Father. But oh Mother, the ducks are going to die! They are drowning! They... they... their feet are up and their head is down."

Mother hurried outside with Amelia. They went to the fence beside the pond.

"Look!" said Amelia. "The duck's head is down in the water. The duck's feet are up. The duck is kicking. It cannot get its head

out of the water. It is going to drown. Oh
Mother, you must help the ducks! It makes
me sad to see the ducks drown. Please
Mother, help the ducks!"

Mother put her hand on Amelia's
shoulder. "The ducks are catching little bugs
and things in the water," she said. "Look,
now the duck's legs go back in the water and
her head comes out of the water."

Amelia looked at the ducks. She saw their heads come back up.

"Are they not drowning?"

"No," said Mother. "It is normal for a duck to do that."

"What does normal mean?" asked Amelia.

"It means that ducks like to do that and they do it often." said Mother.

Amelia sighed. "I'm so glad the ducks are normal," she said.

"The ducks are very normal," said Mother. She laughed a little as she walked back to the house.

Rhyme Time

Ducks on the pond,
Go swim and splash-
and skim and swim-
All day long.
Ducks on the pond,
Go dash and skim-
and kick and dash-
All day long.
Ducks on the pond
Go swim and splash-
and skim and swim-
and dash and skim-
and kick and dash-
All day long.

My New Words

Bess

Beauty

mowing

lawn mower

pretend

team

pockets

handle

obedient

disobedient

giddap

Bess and Beauty

Alvin was mowing the grass. Back and forth he went. He walked fast and the grass flew up in the air.

"I want to do that too," said Amelia. "I want a turn too, Alvin."

"You may have a turn," said Alvin. "I will go in for a drink of water now."

Amelia took the lawn mower. She put her hands on the handle. She pushed, then she pushed some more. The lawn mower moved a little.

Alvin came back. He saw Amelia push. He saw the lawn mower move a little. "You are too little," said Alvin.

"I am not too little."

"You cannot push hard," said Alvin.

Amelia started to cry. Father was in the barn. He heard Amelia. He came to the children.

"What is the matter?" asked Father.

"She is too little to mow the grass," said Alvin. "She cannot push the lawn mower."

"You could help her," said Father. "You take hold on one side. Amelia takes hold on the other side. You can walk beside each other. You can pretend that you are a team of horses."

Amelia stopped crying. She took hold on one side of the handle.

Alvin did not come. He put his hands in his pockets.

"I don't want to," he said. "It is more fun to push it alone. I don't want to mow the lawn with Amelia. I wish she would go away and let me do it."

Father looked at Alvin. Father did not look happy. "I am glad you want to work, Alvin. I want my boy to like doing his work, but I want you to share with Amelia. She wants to mow the grass too. I asked you to help Amelia. If you don't do what I say, you are disobedient. Children who are not obedient are not happy."

Father stopped. He looked at Alvin. Alvin looked at Father, then he looked at the grass. He looked down for a long time.

"You want to be obedient," said Father. Alvin stopped looking down at the grass. He looked at Amelia and Father.

"I will let Amelia help me," he said. "We will pretend we are Bess and Beauty."

He walked over to the lawn mower and took hold on the other handle.

"Giddap!" said Father. "Come on Bess
and Beauty. Let's get the grass mowed."

Alvin kicked up his heels. He was a
happy horse.

"Come on Amelia, let's run," he said.

Away they ran!

Rhyme Time

When the grass grows green,

And its time to cut,

I am mighty keen,

So I strut, strut, strut.

Work comes before play

But I mind it not,

I am bright and gay,

As I strut, strut, strut.

My New Words

hungry   cherry

pie   lemon

cake   hollow

tomorrow   squashed

clapped   shoulders

cupboard   knee

remember

The Funny Pie

"One, two, three, four, five, six, seven," counted Amelia. "Mother made seven pies. It will take us a long time to eat seven pies."

"I want to give some of the pies to Joseph and Ruth," said Mother. "They are building a new barn. The men work hard. They are hungry. I want to make some cakes too. We want to take pies and cakes to Joseph and Ruth tomorrow."

"May I go along?" asked Amelia.

"Yes, you may come with me," said
Mother. "Father and Alvin will come too."

"And Emma," said Amelia. "Emma will
come too."

"Emma will go to Grandfather and
Grandmother." said Mother. "I want to help
Ruth get dinner. Many, many people will be
there. Emma will not be happy there. She
will be happy to stay with Grandfather and
Grandmother."

Amelia clapped her hands. She was
happy to go along to Joseph and Ruth.

"I must get dinner for my own family
now," said Mother. "I must put the pies on
the cupboard. I want to have dinner ready
when Father and Alvin come in."

Amelia got her doll. She started to play.
Then she heard Mother. "Oh look, Amelia! A
big truck is driving past. Part of a house is
on the truck!"

Amelia ran to the window. She tried to

look, but she could not see the truck. She got a chair. She climbed on the chair, then on the cupboard. Oh! Oh! Amelia wanted to see the truck. She did not look on the cupboard. Amelia did not remember the pies on the cupboard.

Amelia's knee went down on a cherry pie. Crash! Amelia's foot bumped against a lemon pie and it fell to the floor. She forgot all about the truck.

Amelia looked at the lemon pie. The plate was upside down. The pie was broken.

Amelia's knee felt warm from the cherry pie. The pie had a hollow spot where Amelia's knee had squashed it. Amelia was not happy. She started to cry. Her tears splashed onto the squashed cherry pie.

Mother came to Amelia. Her shoulders were shaking. She did not want to laugh when Amelia was crying. "It is okay," said Mother. "Five of the pies are still okay to take along. I know you did not want to do

that. After dinner you may help me make the cakes."

Amelia tried to stop crying. She did not feel like laughing but the cherry pie did look funny.

My New Words

swish

wa-a-a

broom

dustpan

reached

comb

elastic

crib

Amelia Helps Mother

"Mother is busy," thought Amelia. "I will help her. Mother is in the garden. I will sweep the floor. When Mother comes in, she will see a clean floor."

"Swish! Swish!" went the broom. Amelia was busy and she was happy.

"Wa-a-a!"

"Oh! Oh! Emma is awake, I must get her!" Amelia went to Emma's crib. "Come

Emma," she said. She helped Emma out of the crib. Emma was still crying a little. "I will get a cookie for you," said Amelia.

Emma stopped crying when she saw the cookie. She broke the cookie in two pieces. She took part of the cookie in each hand.

"Funny Emma," said Amelia, "You are a funny little girl. Your hair is a mess. I will comb you hair while you eat the cookie."

Amelia sat Emma on a chair. She got a comb. Then Amelia saw the broom. "I must finish the floor first," she thought. She picked up the broom and swept the dirt on a pile. She got the dustpan, but she could not get the dirt on the pan. She tried and tried, but she could not get the dirt to stay on the pan.

Amelia looked at the dirt, she wanted the kitchen to be clean when Mother came in. What could she do?

I know! She thought.

She picked up the broom, then she swept the dirt over to the sink. She lifted the mat and swept the dirt under the mat.

"Now I am done with the floor, Emma. Next I will comb your messy hair."

Amelia reached for Emma's hair, she took out the elastic. Emma did not like this. She started to cry. Just then Mother came in.

"Oh Mother!" said Amelia. "I wanted to surprise you. I wanted to comb Emma's hair."

"You wanted to help," said Mother, "but you are too little to comb Emma's hair. I will do that for you."

"I swept the floor," said Amelia.

Mother looked at the floor.

"It is nice and clean," she said. "Thank you Amelia."

"I could not get the dirt on to the dust pan," said Amelia.

"Where did you put the dirt?" asked Mother. "I do not see any dirt."

"I put it under the mat," said Amelia. "I swept all of the dirt under the mat. Now the floor is clean." She smiled at Mother as she spoke.

Mother smiled too. She smiled and smiled and then she laughed.

"You are a good helper," said Mother. "I like when you help, come I will show you how to sweep dirt on to the dust pan. A good helper like you can learn how to do that."

My New Words

chores

enough

stool

grabbed

rather

important

chicken

willingly

size

Father's Big Helper

Alvin liked to help father with the chores. He gave the cows and horses some hay. He gave Rover and Tiger some milk.

"I could milk the cow," said Alvin. "I am big enough now to milk the cow."

"You need strong hands to milk a cow," said Father.

"My hands are strong," said Alvin. "Please Father, may I milk the cow."

"You may try," said Father.

Alvin got the pail and the little stool. He sat down beside the cow. He knew how to milk a cow. He had watched Father milk a cow. Now he knew just how to do it.

Alvin grabbed the cow. He wanted the milk to go into the pail.

Alvin's hands did not feel like Father's hands. The cow did not like when Alvin grabbed it. She stepped away from Alvin.

"Whoa cow!" said Alvin.

He moved his stool closer to the cow and tried again.

Splat! The cow's tail slapped across Alvin's face. It stung his face and his hat fell off.

Alvin got up. He was crying. The cow stepped over. It stepped on Alvin's hat.

"I do not want to milk the cow," he said, "She does not keep nice and still."

"Six is rather little to milk a cow," said Father. "If you want more chores to do I will teach you how to take care of the hens. I think a boy your size is just the right size to learn how to feed the hens.

Alvin watched Father milk the cow. It looked so easy.

"Milking a cow is more important than feeding hens," said Alvin. "I want to do something big."

"A cow is bigger than a chicken," said Father, "but it is not more important, if you learn to take care of the chickens you will be a big help to me. Some work may seem bigger or more important, but it is not the size that counts. Do you know what is most important of all?"

Alvin thought a little. He could not think what was the most important of all. He shook his head.

"The most important of all," said Father. "Is that we do our work willingly, and try to do it the best we can. If you willingly do what I ask you to do you are a big help to me."

"Even if I can't milk the cow?" asked Alvin.

"Yes, even if you can't milk the cow. If you are willing to do whatever I ask you to do and don't grumble at your work then you are my big helper."

Alvin smiled. It felt good to know that Father thought he was a big helper even if he couldn't milk the cow.

My New Words

pickles

picnic

sandwiches

oars

paddles

rowed

shade

basket

Pickles For Lunch

Mother was busy. She was putting things into a basket.

"Amelia, please go downstairs and get some pickles," she said.

"Will we have pickles?" asked Amelia. "I don't think pickles are good for a picnic."

"Wait and see," said Mother. "We will take pickles for our lunch. We will see if they are good."

Amelia went to get the pickles. Mother put the jar into the basket.

Father got Star. The family was ready to go. Away they went.

They came to a river. Father tied Star to the fence.

"We will go for a boat ride first," he said. "Who wants a boat ride?"

"I do!" said Alvin. He ran down to the boat.

"I don't!" said Amelia, she backed away from the river.

"Come," said Father. "I will take your hand. I will help you get into the boat."

Mother carried Emma. Soon they were all in the boat.

Father and Alvin sat in the middle. They made the boat go. Amelia sat very close to Mother and Emma. She did not want to fall into the water.

"Those are big spoons," said Amelia. "Big wooden spoons to make the boat go."

"These are oars or paddles," said Father.

It was fun to ride in the boat. Amelia looked at the water. She could see fish in the water.

"I am getting hungry," said Father. "Let's go back to our lunch."

Father and Alvin turned the boat around. They rowed the boat back to where Star was tied to the fence.

"Where will we eat?" asked Alvin.

"We could sit beside the big tree," said Mother. "It would be nice and cool in the shade."

Soon the family was eating the lunch that Mother had put into the basket. Amelia got a sandwich.

"Ham! I like ham sandwiches," she said.

"Ham sandwiches with a pickle," said Mother, as she bit into a pickle.

She smiled at Amelia.

Amelia watched Mother then she slowly got a pickle from the jar. She took a bite

from her sandwich then a bite from her pickle.

"Mmm, this is good!" she said. "This is much better than I thought it would be."

"Every picnic lunch is good with pickles," said Mother.

"Every picnic lunch is good," said Alvin. "Thank you for the good lunch, Mother."

My New Words

pony   trouble

colt   hitch

kitten   Andrew

puppy   Matthew

puppies   reins

flowerbed   ditch

enough   patience

May We Have A Pony?

"See the baby horse," said Amelia. "See Star's baby horse."

"That is a colt," said Alvin.

"A colt?" asked Amelia. "That is a funny word. That's Star's baby. It is a baby horse."

"Alvin is right," said Mother. "A baby horse is called a colt."

"A baby cat is a kitten," said Amelia. "I know that a baby cat is called a kitten. A baby dog is a puppy. I like puppies and kittens."

"I wish we had a puppy," said Alvin.

"I don't wish for a puppy," said Mother.

"Puppies dig in the garden and in the flowerbed. I have enough trouble with Rover. I don't wish for another dog or puppy."

"I am happy that we have a colt," said Amelia. "Father can make a little cart then we can hitch the colt to the cart. Alvin and I can drive the colt."

"Oh, no!" said Mother." You cannot drive the colt. The colt is a baby. It is too little to drive."

"Andrew and Matthew have a colt," said Amelia. "They have a little cart to ride in. I wish we had a little cart."

"That is a pony cart," said Alvin. "Andrew and Matthew have a pony. A colt is not a pony. A pony is like a little horse."

"I wish we had a pony," said Amelia. "Mother may we have a pony?"

"Now now," said Mother. "You and Alvin are too little to drive a pony. You must wait until you are bigger. When a pony wants to run fast, you and Alvin are too little to make it stop."

Amelia thought about what Mother had said. She thought about Andrew and Matthew's pony. Andrew and Matthew had to hold the reins. When the pony ran fast they pulled on the reins. Andrew and Matthew were bigger than Alvin and Amelia. They were strong. They could pull hard. They could make the pony stop.

"Mother! Mother! I know what we can do! There are two reins. Alvin and I are two people, Alvin can hold one rein. I can hold one rein. We can pull hard. We can make the pony stop. Please Mother, may we have a pony now?"

"No," said Mother. "If you pull on one rein, and Alvin pulls on the other rein, it will

not work. If Alvin pulls harder than you do, the pony will turn. It might run into the ditch. No, you must wait for a pony until you are bigger."

Amelia sat down to think. She did not want a pony to run into the ditch.

"Mother," she said. "I will grow fast. I will grow big and strong so that I can have a pony."

"Patience, patience," said Mother. "You are growing up fast enough."

My New Words

thankful

ointment

sandbox

supper

plates

angry

Thankful For Emma

Emma was crying. She cried a lot the last while.

"She is cutting teeth," said Mother.

"Cutting teeth?" asked Amelia. "Oh, Mother how can Emma cut teeth?"

"She is growing teeth," said Mother. "When the teeth push through the gums we say she is cutting teeth."

"Why does she cry?" asked Amelia. Is

she not happy to have more teeth?"

"It hurts," said Mother. "Her gums are sore. I will put this ointment on. It will help her gums to feel better then you can take her to the sandbox. She likes it in the sandbox."

Amelia and Emma played in the sandbox. Amelia made little houses and roads. When Emma stepped on the houses Amelia did not get angry. Amelia knew that she could make more houses.

Emma walked over to the flowerbed. Amelia made more houses in the sand.

Then Father and Alvin came in from the barn. It was supper time. Amelia went to the house too.

"Where is Emma?" asked Mother.

"She went to the flowers," said Amelia. "I thought she will go to the house."

Everyone went outside. They looked and looked for Emma.

"Emma! Emma!" called Father.

"Emma! Emma!" called Mother.

Amelia started to cry. What if they could not find Emma? She sat down on the steps and cried and cried.

"Look at Rover," said Alvin." Rover is not in his house. Only Rover's nose is in the house."

"That is strange," said Father. "I will go and look." Father ran to Rover's house. He looked inside.

"I found her!" he said. "Emma is in Rover's house!"

The family ran to the dog house. There was Emma. She was fast asleep. Everyone looked at Emma. She looked so cute!

"We will not wake her," said Mother. "We will let her sleep. She has cried so much today because her gums hurt."

"We can eat out here," said Father. "We will bring our plates out here."

The family went in. They thanked God for keeping Emma safe and for helping them

to find her.

"I will never forget how we lost Emma," said Amelia. "I am so thankful that we found her."

My New Words

turtle

snapping

Lloyd

stomach

tremble

pester

sneak

Will It Bite?

Rover was barking. He barked and barked. He was barking at something in the grass.

"Why is Rover barking?" asked Mother. "Alvin, please go and see why Rover is barking."

Alvin ran outside. He looked in the grass. Amelia ran too. She ran after Alvin.

"A turtle!" said Alvin. "There is a turtle

in the grass! Stay away, Amelia! I will run and get Father."

Away Alvin ran! Soon he came back. Father was with him.

"It is a snapping turtle," said Father. "He got a stick. He put the stick close to the turtle's head. The turtle opened its mouth. It snapped at the stick."

"Can it bite hard?" asked Amelia.

"Oh yes," said Father. You would not want a turtle to bite your finger."

Amelia took a few steps away from the turtle.

"Turtles cannot run fast," said Father. "If you stay away this turtle will not get you."

"Where do turtles live?" asked Alvin.

"They like to be close to water," said Father. "They like to swim."

"What will we do with it? Will we keep it for a pet?"

"A snapping turtle is not a good pet," said Father. "Some turtles are very little. A little turtle would be a good pet, but a big snapping turtle is not a good pet. I think I will ask Lloyd what we should do."

Soon Lloyd came with his truck. He put the turtle into his truck.

"I will take the turtle to the river," he said. "It will be happier in the river than here on dry land."

"Will he take it to the river where we went boating and had our picnic?" asked Alvin.

"Yes, I think so," said Father.

Amelia's stomach felt funny. She thought about the boat ride and the picnic.

"We cannot have a picnic again," she said. "We cannot have a boat ride."

"Why?" asked Alvin.

Father looked at Amelia. He saw her lips tremble. He saw that Amelia was afraid. He got down in front of Amelia.

"Tell me what is the matter," he said. "Tell me what you are afraid of."

"Lloyd will take the turtle to the river. You said that a snapping turtle will bite hard. If we go for a boat ride or picnic, the turtle will bite us. I do not want the turtle to bite us."

"Turtles do not bite us if we do not pester them," said Father. "They will stay away from us. A turtle will not sneak up to us and bite us. They do not like people and they will stay away from us."

Amelia's lips stopped trembling and turned into a smile. She was glad to hear that turtles did not bother you if you did not bother them.

My New Words

husking

cob

wheelbarrow

kernels

guess

welcome

true

breakfast

women

carrying

tomorrow

Husking Corn

"Grandfather and Grandmother will come tomorrow," said Mother.

"Oh, good!" said Amelia. "I like when they come. I like when they look at books with us. I like when they tell us stories."

"There will be no time to look at books this time," said Mother. "The corn is ready. Tomorrow we want to cut up a lot of corn."

"May I help?" asked Amelia.

"Yes," said Mother. "You may help to husk the corn. Father and Grandfather will help too, Grandmother and I will cut the corn from the cobs. It will be a busy day."

The next day Father went to the garden after breakfast. He came back with a wheelbarrow load of corn.

Just then Grandfather and Grandmother came driving in the lane.

Soon the whole family was outside. They husked the green leaves from the ears of corn. The women started to cut the kernels from the cobs. Father went back to the garden for more corn.

"We are a busy family," said Amelia. "We are a busy corn family. I like husking corn."

"I like to carry the husks to the cows," said Alvin. "That is the best part about husking corn."

"Is it really?" asked Grandfather. "Is that the part you like best?"

"Yes," said Alvin. "That is the best part

of all."

"I like husking," said Grandfather. "I like to see the family working together, but there is something that is better yet."

"What is it?" asked Amelia.

"Guess," said Grandfather.

Alvin and Amelia looked at Grandfather. They did not know what is better than husking corn or carrying the husks away. Father brought the corn from the garden. Grandmother and Mother cut the kernels from the cob. What was better? What did Grandfather like better?

"I like to eat corn," said Grandfather.

Everyone laughed. Yes, eating was the best part of all.

"I wish you would tell us a story," said Alvin. "Can you tell us a story while we husk corn?"

Just then Tiger came around the corner of the house. She came to the family. She rubbed against the bowl of corn cobs.

"Go away, Tiger!" said Amelia. "We do not want you here now."

Tiger walked away. When Amelia talked like that Tiger knew he was not welcome.

"Grandmother and I will go inside now," said Mother. We will put this corn into jars, then we will come outside and cut some more."

"Do you have a story ready?" asked Alvin.

"What stories do you like best?" asked Grandfather.

"I like true stories best," said Alvin. "Can you tell us a true story?"

"Tell us about when you were a little boy," said Amelia. "I like stories about when you were a little boy."

"Yes! Yes!" said Alvin. "I like those stories best of all."

My New Words

interrupt	unwillingly
quite	worry
returned	worried
Scamper	obey
hunted	mattress
nobody	straw
whole	gasped

Grandfather's Story

"When I was a little boy," began Grandfather. "We got a new puppy."

"I wish we would," said Alvin.

"I do too," said Amelia.

"Let Grandfather tell his story," said Father. "Don't interrupt when he is talking."

"The puppy was still quite small when we lost him one day."

"Lost him!" gasped Amelia.

"Don't interrupt." said Alvin.

"Oh," said Amelia.

"I had gone to town with my Father and returned home at supper time. After supper I wanted to play with Scamper I couldn't find him. I hunted and hunted for him but I..."

"Did nobody help you?" asked Alvin.

"Don't interrupt," said Amelia.

"Yes the whole family helped to look for him, but we couldn't find him. Mother said its time for me to go to bed. I went quite unwillingly as I was worried about Scamper. I thought I have to find him before I go to bed."

"Did you cry?" asked Amelia.

"Yes, I did," said Grandfather. "When I had to go to bed without finding him, I cried. I wanted to obey Mother, but it was hard to go to bed. It was good that I obeyed. It is always good to obey. Yes, the best thing that I could have done is obey my Mother and jump into bed. I had just jumped into bed when I heard Scamper barking."

"Where was he?" asked Alvin.

"It is hard to believe," said Grandfather, "but Scamper was inside the mattress, on my bed. I had a mattress that was filled with straw. That afternoon my sisters had taken out the old straw and put in fresh straw."

"And they put the puppy in!" shouted Amelia.

"No they didn't put him in," said Grandfather. "No one knows how it happened, but we think the puppy crawled in when no one was watching and then fell asleep. When I got into bed Scamper woke up and started barking."

"Did you let him out?" asked Amelia.

"I don't think Rover could hide in our bed," said Alvin.

"Yes I let the puppy out," said Grandfather. "Now my story is finished and you two may talk. I think both of you are

good at interrupting."

Alvin and Amelia looked at each other. Both of them thought the other one had interrupted the story. It was hard to not interrupt when Grandfather was telling a story.

My New Words

school

wishing   questions

lunch pail   baseball

shiny   sandwich

grapes   Teacher

chocolate

neatly

listen

Alvin Goes To School

Amelia was not happy. Alvin could go to school, but she could not.

"I wish I were six," she said. "If I were six I could go to school."

"You are not six," said Alvin. "If you are not six you must stay at home."

Amelia knew that Alvin was right. Just wishing she were older would not help. The best thing she could do was to be happy even if she could not go to school with Alvin.

Alvin had a new blue lunch pail. Amelia helped Mother to put lunch into the shiny new lunch pail. Alvin had a sandwich and carrots in his lunch. He had an apple and some grapes, but what Alvin would like best of all was a chocolate chip cookie.

"Good bye," said Alvin.

"Good bye," said Amelia.

"Good bye," said Mother. "Be a good boy at school. Do your work neatly and listen to your Teacher."

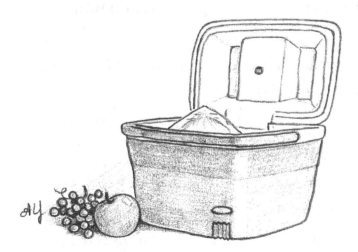

Alvin walked to the end of the lane.
Andrew and Matthew were coming. He would
get a ride with the pony cart.

It was a long day for Amelia, but she
tried to be happy. She could not play with
Alvin, but she could play with Emma.

When Alvin came home Amelia had many
questions for him.

"Was it fun at school? What did you do?
Did you color? Did you count? Did you print
your name? Where did you sit? Did you eat
all your lunch?"

"Stop! Stop!" said Mother. "You must not

ask the questions so fast. You must let Alvin have some time to answer your questions before you ask the next one."

Alvin took some papers from his pocket.

"I did all of this," he said. "I did some pages in a book too."

Amelia looked and looked at the papers. How she wished that she were six and could go to school too.

"I like it at school," said Alvin. "I had a lot of fun, when it was time to play we played baseball. Matthew helped me to hit the ball."

"Do you wish you could be at school all the time?" asked Amelia. "Do you like it better than here at home?"

"I like it at school," said Alvin. "I think school is fun, but I am glad to be at home too."

"Will you still like playing with me?" asked Amelia.

"Oh yes!" said Alvin. "All day I did not

see you. Now I want to play with you and Emma. Come let's go to the sandbox."

Amelia smiled. It would be fun to play in the sandbox with Alvin and Emma.

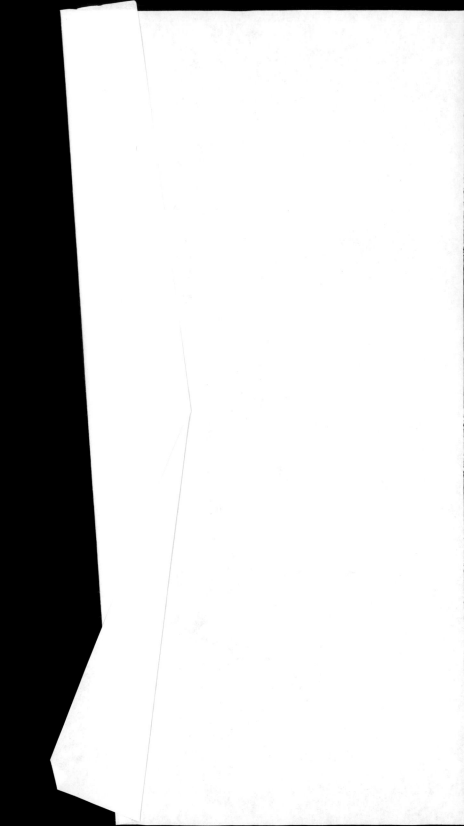